The Snail and the Whale Sticker Book

Don't forget to decorate this page with your stickers

This book belongs to

. . . .

Then colour it in!

Julia Donaldson   Axel Scheffler

MACMILLAN CHILDREN'S BOOKS

Harbour Sticker Scene

This is a tale of a tiny snail . . .

And They All Set Sail . . .

Use your stickers to complete the sunset scene.

How many snails can you fit on the whale's tail?

Sticker Shadows

Who did the snail meet on his trip?
Find the sticker and match it to the right shadow.

Sticker Games

Look at the three patterns below, then use your stickers to complete each one.

Colouring

Colour in this picture of the snail and his flock.

_____ What colour will the sky be?

Is it a sunny day? ~~~~

Now use your stickers to make this picture match the one on the left.

Count them up! Did you find all ten?

Spot the Difference Sticker Game

Can you spot ten differences between these two scenes?

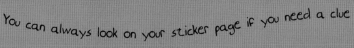

You can always look on your sticker page if you need a clue

Save the whale! Use your stickers to fill the beach with people to help him.

 Quick, quick! He needs your help!

Sticker Scene

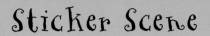

"I can't move on land! I'm too big!" moaned the whale.

Colouring

What do you think the children are pointing at?

Draw it on the blackboard, then colour in the picture.

Now draw your own pictures.

You could draw the snail's adventures, or you could make up your own!

Complete the Picture

Can you fill the sea with racing speedboats?

Look on your sticker page to find the speedboats

What a racket!

Who Lives Here?

The snail met lots of interesting creatures on his adventure with the whale.

Who did they see . . .

. . . in sunny warm trees?

Use your stickers to complete each picture

. . . on the smooth black rock?

. . . on the shimmering ice?

. . . beneath the waves?

. . . on the golden sand?

Sticker Jigsaws

Use your square jigsaw stickers to complete these pictures.

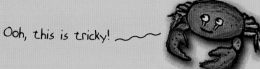
Ooh, this is tricky!

Sticker Shadows

Fill this underwater scene with fish.

Use your stickers!

Extra Stickers

Extra Stickers

Sticker Scene

Sticker Games

Sticker Shadows

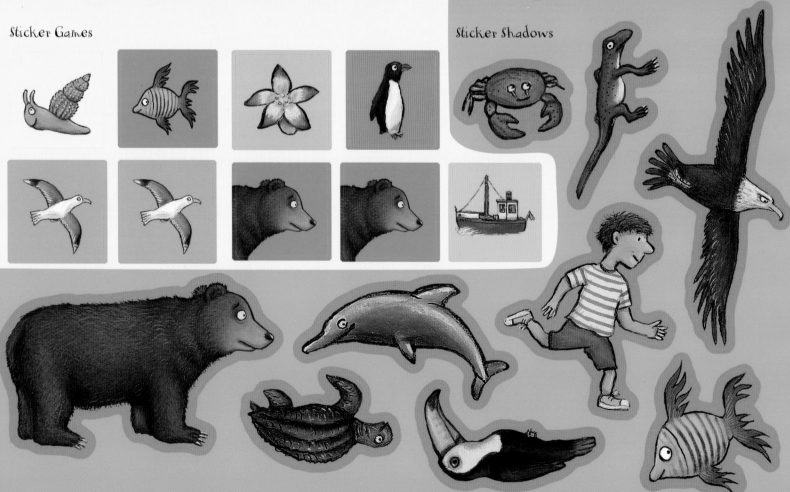

Sticker Jigsaws

Who Lives Here?

Spot the Difference Sticker Game

Complete the Picture

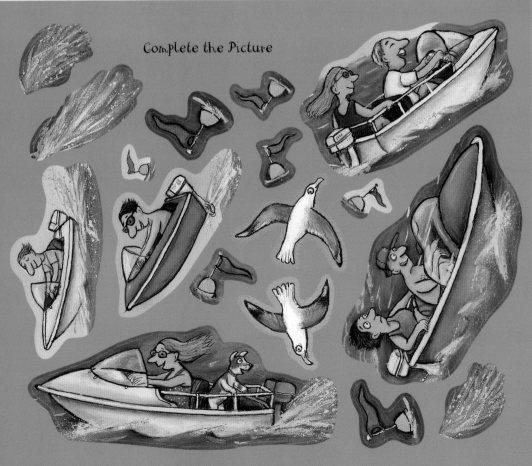

And They All Set Sail . . .

Spot the Difference Sticker Game

Beach Sticker Scene

Wordsearch

Sticker Shadows

This book belongs to . . .

Sticker Jigsaw

Complete the Picture

Decorate a Snail

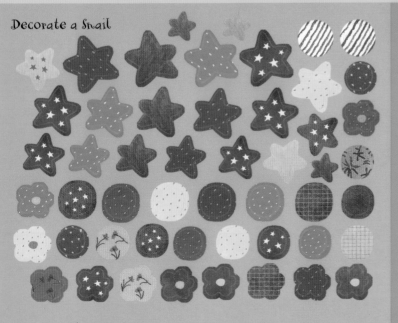

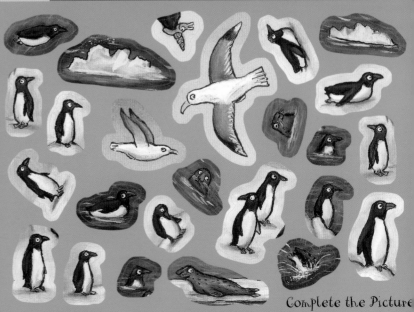

Complete the Picture

Wordsearch

Look carefully . . .

They're all in there somewhere!

Can you spot all these words in the grid below?
When you find the word, add the matching sticker.

WAVES

CHILDREN

SNAIL

MOON

PENGUIN

VOLCANO

N	T	E	A	G	H	E	R	H	W
B	L	A	C	K	B	O	A	R	D
R	T	O	O	I	P	A	V	M	P
E	U	N	W	H	A	L	E	F	E
W	A	V	E	S	S	B	S	I	N
G	H	I	S	N	A	I	L	R	G
A	M	O	O	N	L	P	A	E	U
E	E	L	A	H	W	A	I	M	I
V	O	L	C	A	N	O	L	E	N
D	G	H	I	L	D	R	E	N	B

TEACHER

WHALE

BLACKBOARD

FIREMEN

Use your stickers to complete the tropical island scene.

Watch out for the volcano!

Beach Sticker Scene

This is the sea, so wild and free . . .

What might you find on the beach?

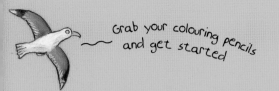
Colouring

These are the caves
Beneath the waves.

Watch out for sharks!

Follow the key to colour in the picture.

1 yellow   3 blue   5 green   7 grey

2 pink   4 red   6 purple   8 orange

Complete the Picture

Use your stickers to cover this iceberg with penguins.

What else can you add to the scene?

This is the whale who came one night
When the tide was high and the stars were bright.

If you get stuck, check your sticker page!

Count them up – did you find ten?

Spot the Difference Sticker Game

Can you spot ten differences between these two scenes?

Now use your stickers to make the picture below match the one above.

Decorate a Snail

Design some new shells for these snails and colour them in.
You could use your stickers or make up your own patterns.

They can look like me!

How pretty!

Complete the Picture

How many snails can you squeeze on the rock?

Use your snail stickers

Sticker Jigsaw

Use your square jigsaw stickers to complete the picture.

The harbour is looking very quiet! Use your stickers to bring it to life.

Don't forget the snail!